THE OWL THAT DIDN'T KNOW HOW

By Joe Atkinson

Illustration by Alma Caicedo

To Amber
Joe was here.

Meet Mr Owl.

You might say to him 'How d'you do Mr Owl?'

And his reply would be 'HOW d'you do little one?' And when Mr Owl says HOW about anything, he really means HOW.

How do I know. Let me tell you the story.

Mr Owl lived in a tree high up in the forest. Every day he would look out into this great forest and with wonder he would think –

HOW does everything work?
HOW did that tree get next to that tree?
HOW did that sun move across the sky?

HOW did this? HOW did that? HOW did it?

So the incredibly curious Mr Owl had an idea.
One day, instead of sitting on his branch and
wondering HOW?
He decided to find out HOW.

He took off and flew down to the ground and stood next to a small rabbit that could hop at great speeds.

'HOW do you run?' He asked the Rabbit.

'Well just like this,' replied the Rabbit and he bounced off using his back legs to spring up through the grass.

He flew up through the undergrowth of the forest and found an elephant stomping through the forest. As he landed on this elephant's trunk he asked

"HOW did you grow so big?"

The elephant turned his head towards the owl and replied, "I eat all that the forest has to offer me and eat everything that my mother showed me I am allowed to eat, which is an awful lot of the forest"

And off he stomped, every so often stopping to chomp and chew on the leaves on the trees.

And so Mr Owl flew off again and
he saw a very old looking shed
under the shade of some trees.
He landed on the window sill and
looked into the Shed.
In the window he saw another Owl
that looked exactly like the curious
Mr Owl. He stared in amazement.

"How did you grow to look exactly
like me?" he asked.

And he waited. But there was no reply. This Owl is awfully rude he thought and he flew off.

And as he flew away he noticed a chimney and out of the chimney there was a long line of smoke filling the sky air.

"HOW did you get here smoke?" he said to himself and obviously the smoke did not reply because smoke can't talk and the owl realised this and he thought to himself HOW come you cannot talk and I can talk and then he flew off.

As he flew further he noticed a tiny army of ants marching up and down carrying leaves that were bigger than the ants themselves.

"HOW can you carry something so big?" he whispered to the group of ants.

And one ant placed the little bit of leaf he was carrying on the floor, stood up proud and shouted "we just pick them up, put them on our backs and off we go."

And the Owl flew off, higher and higher into the sky and into the clouds and he saw the clouds and he thought "HOW did you get up here if you don't have any wings?"

And a cloud that made the shape of an old man with a walking stick said "we are so light that we flow with the wind and get blown around into all sorts of different shapes and sizes"

And he flew down low and discovered a puddle of water in an opening on the forest floor. He stared into the puddle and again he saw that exact same owl that he had seen in the shed window earlier. The owl was looking right back at him again.

"HOW did you get in there!?" He asked and again the rude owl did not reply.

It was getting dark now and the owl wondered if all of his HOW questions had been answered for the day and if he had learnt anything and he thought to himself that he wasn't too sure if he had learnt anything or not!

And he thought and thought about this. And the question that came into his mind when he thought about this was

"HOW do I know if I found out the things that I didn't know HOW?"

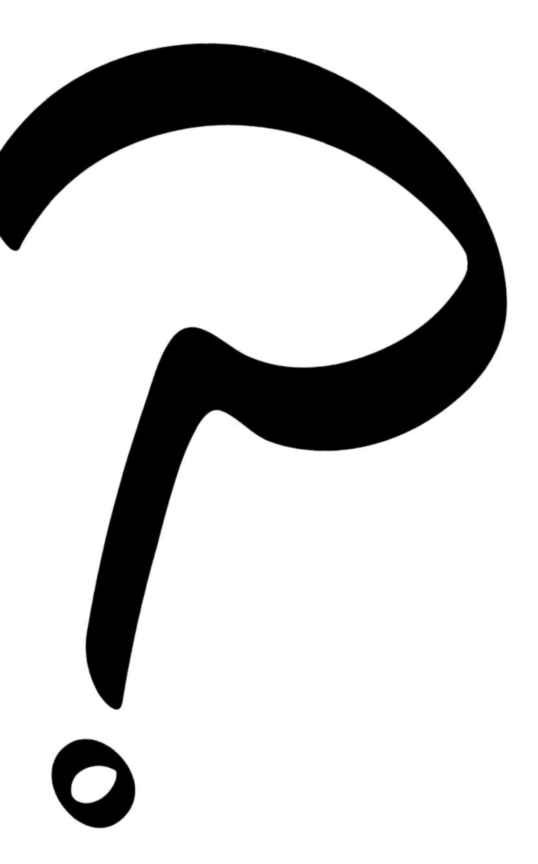

And out of all the questions he asked on that day he liked this question the most and he liked the sound of the word HOW and he said it over and over HOW HOW HOW HOW.

And as he flew back to his nest high up in the forest he sang to himself.

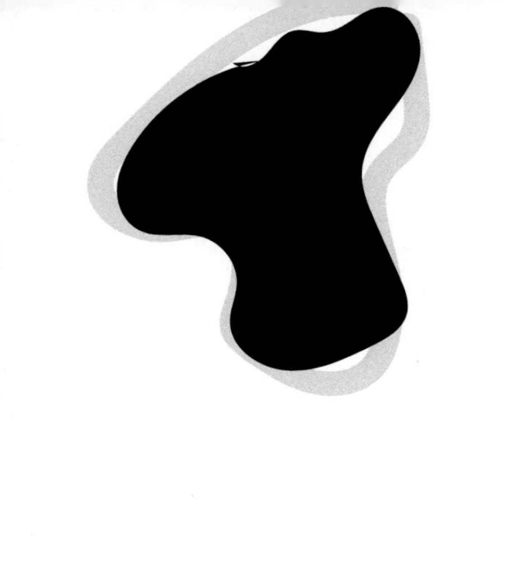
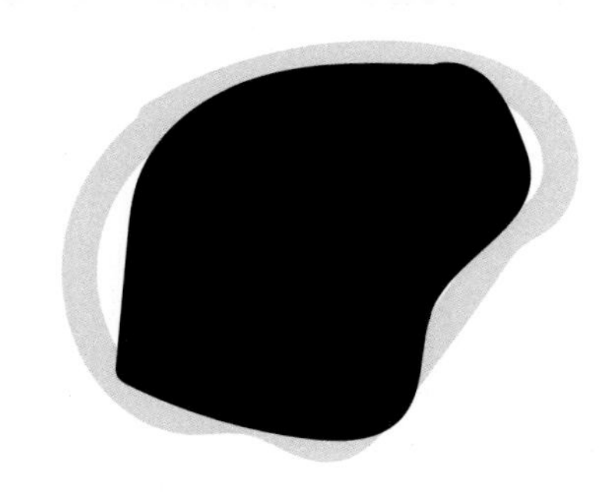

HOW HOW HOW

HOW NOW...HOW NOW....HOW NOW

HOW NOW COW....HOW NOW COW....
HOW NOW COW

HOW NOW BROWN COW....HOW NOW BROWN COW....
HOW NOW BROWN COW

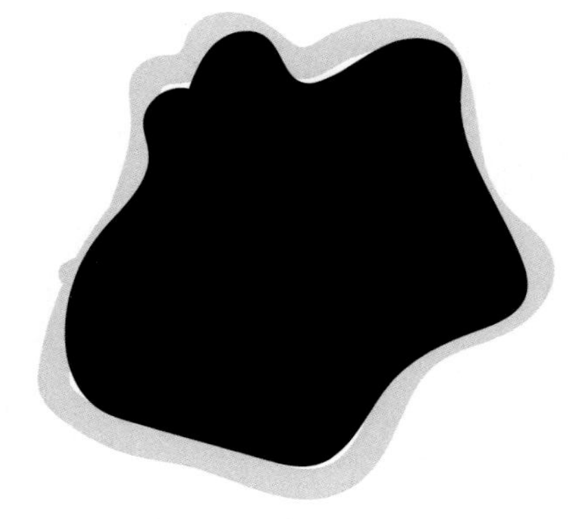
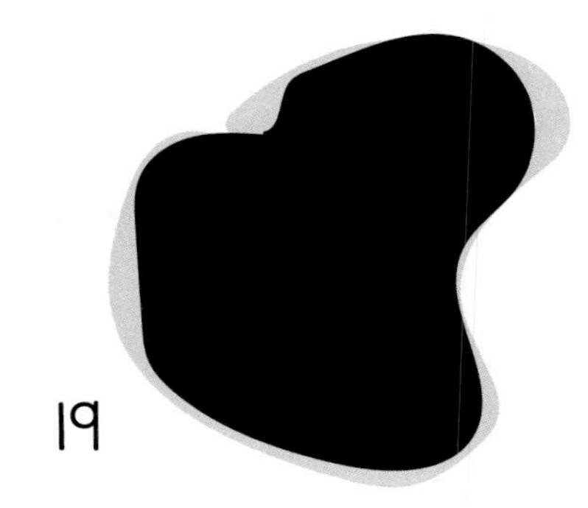

And he got to his nest and he fell asleep.
He wasn't too sure if he had found out HOW about anything at all but he enjoyed the day very much and he wondered what things he would like to try and find out about different HOWS tomorrow.

And the very next day he woke up he looked into the forest and a tree had fallen over and his nest had come crashing to the ground and some other parts of the forest had been destroyed and the owl thought.

WHY

The Owl that didn´t know how

By Joe Atkinson

Illustration

By Alma Caicedo